IMP

First published 1985 © International Music Publications
Exclusive Distributors: International Music Publications, Southend Road, Woodford Green, Essex IG8 8HN, England
215-2-271, Order ref: 09907, ISBN 0.86359.243.0
Cover design by Howard Brown/Peter Wood. Photography by Peter Wood

ALL THE THINGS YOU ARE

Words by OSCAR HAMMERSTEIN II
Music by JEROME KERN

found my ad - ven - ture, Touch-ing your hand, my heart beats the fast - er,

All that I want in all of this world is you.

REFRAIN

You are the prom-ised kiss of spring-time That

makes the lone - ly win - ter seem long

ANYTHING GOES

Words and Music
by COLE PORTER

Moderato

VERSE

Times have changed And we've of-ten re - wound the clock

Cm   Ab   Fm Cm   G7 Cm

Since the Pu - ri-tans got a shock When they land-ed on

Db   Ab7 Db   G7

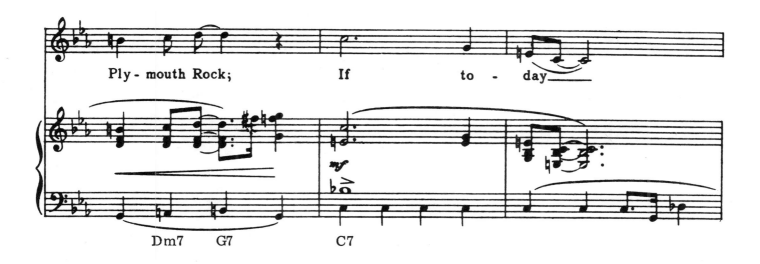

Ply - mouth Rock;   If   to - day____

Dm7   G7   C7

A - ny shock they should try   to stem,   'Stead of land-ing on

C7   Fm   C7   Fm   G7

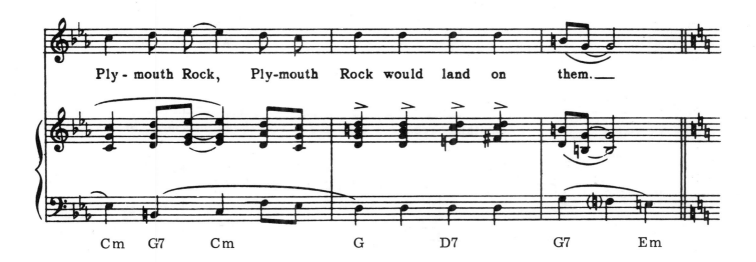

Ply - mouth Rock,   Ply-mouth   Rock would   land   on   them.____

Cm   G7   Cm   G   D7   G7   Em

8

REFRAIN

In old-en days a glimpse of stock-ing Was look'd on as some-thing shock-ing, Now heav-en knows,_____ A-ny-thing goes._____ Good auth-ors too who once knew bet-ter words Now on-ly use four-let-ter words, writ-ing prose,_____ A-ny-thing goes. The world has gone mad to-day And good's

ALL OF ME

SEE P.12 FOR
INTRODUCTION AND VERSE

Words and Music by
SEYMOUR SIMONS and GERALD MARKS

REFRAIN Moderato

INTRODUCTION AND VERSE

I'LL STRING ALONG WITH YOU

Words by AL DUBIN
Music by HARRY WARREN

REFRAIN
Slowly

You may not be an an-gel, 'Cause an-gels are so few,

But un-til the day that one comes a-long, I'll String a-long With You.

I'm look-ing for an an-gel To sing my love song to,

And un-til the day that one comes a-long, I'll sing my song to you.

BYE BYE BLUES

Words and Music by FRED HAMM, DAVE BENNETT,
BERT LOWN and CHAUNCEY GRAY

EMBRACEABLE YOU

Words by IRA GERSHWIN
Music by GEORGE GERSHWIN

REFRAIN (*Rhythmically*)

A FOGGY DAY

Words by IRA GERSHWIN
Music by GEORGE GERSHWIN

REFRAIN (brighter but warmly)

FOR YOU

Words by AL DUBIN
Music by JOE BURKE

GOODY GOODY

Words and Music by
JOHNNY MERCER and MATTY MALNECK

HOMETOWN

Words and Music by
JIMMY KENNEDY and MICHAEL CARR

REFRAIN

I APOLOGISE

Words and Music by AL HOFFMAN,
AL GOODHART and ED NELSON

I'M CONFESSIN' (THAT I LOVE YOU)

Words by AL J NEIBURG
Music by DOC DAUGHERTY and ELLIS REYNOLDS

REFRAIN

I GOT RHYTHM

Words by IRA GERSHWIN
Music by GEORGE GERSHWIN

IT'S ONLY A PAPER MOON

Words by BILLY ROSE and E Y HARBURG
Music by HAROLD ARLEN

REFRAIN

I'VE GOT YOU UNDER MY SKIN

Words and Music
by COLE PORTER

I ONLY HAVE EYES FOR YOU

Words by AL DUBIN
Music by HARRY WARREN

ISLE OF CAPRI

Words by JIMMY KENNEDY
Music by WILHELM GROSZ

Tempo di Tango

VERSE

Some-where far a-way   Ov-er Na-ples bay   That's where my thoughts keep on turn-ing
Soft It-al-ian eyes   Dark as mid-night skies   Sleep-ing or wak-ing they haunt me

Down by the sea_____ Where ro-mance came to me _____
Their mag-ic thrill_____ Holds a spell on me still _____

Pic-tur-ing the scene   And what might have been   But it's in vain that I'm yearn-ing
Tho' I know for me   This love may not be   Why does a sweet voice still taunt me

Fate chang'd it all _____ And I'm left to re - call. _____
Lost love, it seems _____ You just bring emp-ty dreams. _____

Fm   B7   Db7   C Db7   C7

REFRAIN

'Twas on the Isle of Ca-pri that I found her   Beneath the shade of an old wal-nut tree   Oh! I can

F   Gm7   C7

still see the flow'rs blooming round her   Where we met on the Isle of Ca-pri.   She was as

Gm7   C7   F   C7   F

sweet as a rose at the dawn-ing   But somehow fate had-n't meant her for me   And tho' I

F   Gm7   C7

sail'd with the tide in the morn-ing   Still my heart's on the Isle of Ca-pri.

Gm7   C7   F   C7   F

IN A SHANTY IN OLD SHANTY TOWN

Words by JOE YOUNG
Music by LITTLE JACK LITTLE and JOHN SIRAS

52

REFRAIN

IT'S A SIN TO TELL A LIE

Words and Music
by BILLY MAYHEW

I'VE TOLD EV'RY LITTLE STAR

Words by OSCAR HAMMERSTEIN II
Music by JEROME KERN

REFRAIN

THE LADY IS A TRAMP

Words by LORENZ HART
Music by RICHARD RODGERS

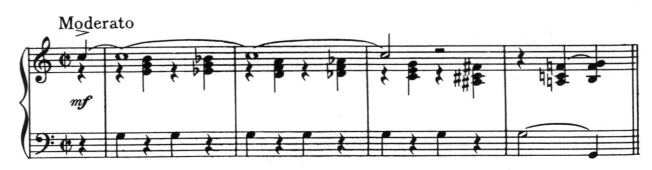

Refrain

I get too hun-gry For din-ner at eight,

I like the thea-tre but nev-er come late.

I nev-er both-er with peo-ple I hate,

That's why the la-dy is a tramp.

I WON'T DANCE

Words by OSCAR HAMMERSTEIN II and OTTO HARBACH
Music by JEROME KERN

1 REFRAIN

SMOKE GETS IN YOUR EYES

Words by OTTO HARBACH
Music by JEROME KERN

8.Eb

Yet to-day____ My love has flown a-way,____ I am with-

B   A♭m7   B♭7

-out my love. Now laugh-ing friends de-

E♭   B♭7/E♭   E♭

-ride Tears I can-not hide._____ So I smile and

B♭7   E♭   E♭+   A♭   A⁰

say, "When a love-ly flame dies, Smoke gets in your eyes."____

E♭maj7   E♭6   Fm7   B♭7   E♭

I'VE GOT THE WORLD ON A STRING

Words by TED KOEHLER
Music by HAROLD ARLEN

REFRAIN

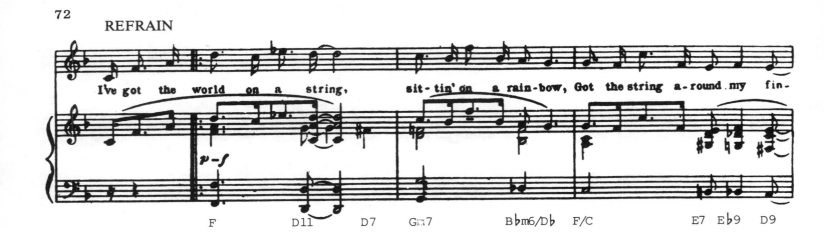

KEEP YOUNG AND BEAUTIFUL

Words by AL DUBIN
Music by HARRY WARREN

What's cute a-bout a lit-tle cu-tie, It's her beau-ty, not
What makes a girls ac-quain-tance big-ger, It's her fig-ure and

brains. Old Fath-er Time will nev-er harm you, If your
poise. Her du-ty should be to re-tain it, To main-

REFRAIN

SOUTH OF THE BORDER

Words and Music by
JIMMY KENNEDY and MICHAEL CARR

PICK YOURSELF UP

Words by DOROTHY FIELDS
Music by JEROME KERN

SEPTEMBER IN THE RAIN

Words by AL DUBIN
Music by HARRY WARREN

LOVE LETTERS IN THE SAND

Words by NICK KENNY and CHAS KENNY
Music by J FRED COOTS

VERSE

1. The sun-beams kissed the sands, My fate was in your hands, The day I
2. While pre-cious tear-drops fall, Your mem'ry I re-call, And days that

met you dear._____ And though I find you gone, Your mem'ry
used to be._____ The skies were blue a-bove, It was the

lin-gers on,— I can't for-get you dear._____ On a
dawn of love, But you've for-got-ten me._____ On a

REFRAIN

PARADISE

Words by NACIO HERB BROWN and GORDON CLIFFORD
Music by NACIO HERB BROWN

REFRAIN

And then {she he} holds my hand, Mm _____ Then Cu-pid

takes com-mand, Mm _____ {Her His} eyes re-

-veal a love that's real, And the sweet smile I

see Brings heav'n to me!___ And then {her his} lips meet

RED SAILS IN THE SUNSET

Words and Music by
JIMMY KENNEDY and HUGH WILLIAMS

SEPTEMBER SONG

Words by MAXWELL ANDERSON
Music by KURT WEILL

VERSE

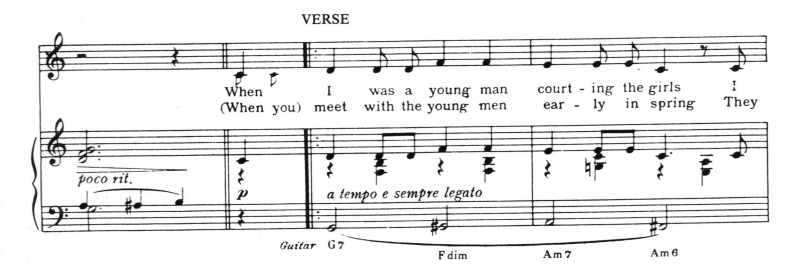

When I was a young man court-ing the girls I
(When you) meet with the young men ear-ly in spring They

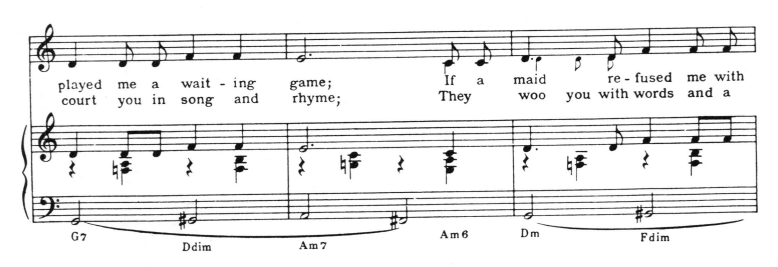

played me a wait-ing game; If a maid re-fused me with
court you in song and rhyme; They woo you with words and a

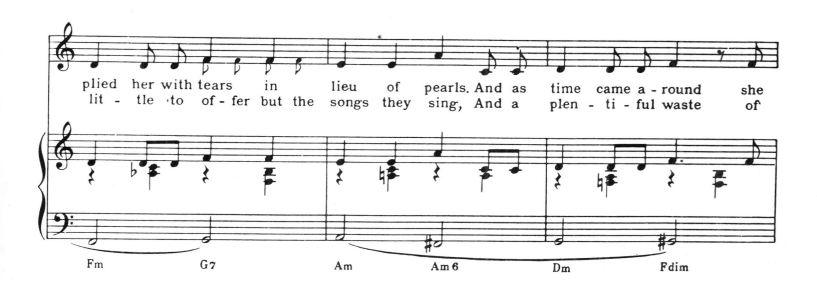

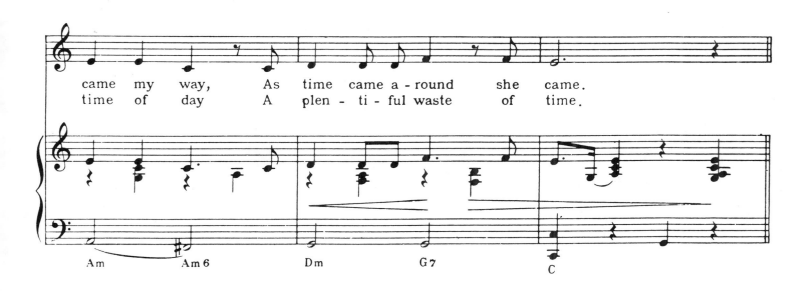

REFRAIN (*with expression*)

But it's a long, long while From May to De - cem - ber;

And the days grow short _____ When you reach Sep - tem - ber;

And the au-tumn wea - ther turns the leaves to flame,

And I have-n't got time _____ for the wait-ing game;

STAY AS SWEET AS YOU ARE

Words and Music by
MACK GORDON and HARRY REVEL

THERE'S A SMALL HOTEL

Words by LORENZ HART
Music by RICHARD RODGERS

WALKIN' MY BABY BACK HOME

Words and Music by
ROY TURK and FRED E AHLERT

THE WAY YOU LOOK TONIGHT

Words by DOROTHY FIELDS
Music by JEROME KERN

WHAT A DIFF'RENCE A DAY MADE

Music and Spanish Words by MARIA GREVER
English Words by STANLEY ADAMS

WHERE OR WHEN

Words by LORENZ HART
Music by RICHARD RODGERS

YOU MUST HAVE BEEN A BEAUTIFUL BABY

Words by JOHNNY MERCER
Music by HARRY WARREN

YOUNG AND HEALTHY

Words by AL DUBIN
Music by HARRY WARREN

VERSE

I know a bun-dle of hu-man-i-ty, she's a-bout so high;_____ I'm near-ly driv-en to in-san-i-ty,

when she pass - es by. She's a snoot-y lit - tle cut - ie, she's

been so hard to kiss; I'll try to o - ver-come her

van - i - ty, and then I'll tell her this:

REFRAIN

I'm young and health - y, and you've got charms;

Printed in Great Britain by Hobbs the Printers of Southampton 6/87